# National 5
# French

## Practice Papers for SQA Exams

Douglas Angus

## Contents

FREE audio files to accompany this title can be accessed at www.hoddereducation.co.uk/updatesandextras

HODDER
GIBSON
AN HACHETTE UK COMPANY

The Publishers would like to thank the following for permission to reproduce copyright material:

**Acknowledgements p.3** 'Les cambrioleurs appellent la police !' adapted from 'Suède : menacés par leur victime, des cambrioleurs appellent la police' in *Le Parisien*, 12 January 2016 (http://www.leparisien.fr/faits-divers/suede-menaces-par-leur-victime-des-cambrioleurs-appellent-la-police-12-01-2016-5443953.php); **p.5** 'Un petit garçon sauve son père à vélo' adapted from 'Mayenne : à 5 ans, il sauve son père après un incroyable périple à vélo' in *Le Parisien*, 8 January 2016 (http://www.leparisien.fr/faits-divers/mayenne-a-5-ans-il-sauve-son-pereapres-un-incroyable-periple-a-velo-08-01-2016-5432219.php) and 'À 5 ans, le petit garçon sauve la vie de son père' in *Ouest France*, 7 January 2016 (http://www.ouest-france.fr/leditiondusoir/data/653/reader/reader.html?t=1452187532267#!preferred/1/package/653/pub/654/page/11); **p.35** article adapted from 'Sécurité. Des lycées veulent autoriser les élèves à fumer dans la cour' in *Ouest France*, 3 February 2016 (http://www.ouest-france.fr/societe/securite-des-lycees-veulent-autoriser-les-eleves-fumer-dans-la-cour-4013031); **p.37** article adapted from 'Grâce à son service européen, elle décroche un job' in *Ouest France*, 23 September 2015 (http://jactiv.ouest-france.fr/job-formation/travailler/grace-son-service-europeen-elle-decroche-job-54297). The following are reproduced with the permission of the Scottish Qualifications Authority: **pp.49–52** National 5 French Assessment Criteria for Writing taken from SQA National 5 French Marking Instructions; **pp.9, 25, 39** adapted from SQA writing questions; **pp.3, 9, 10, 14, 19, 25, 26, 29, 33, 39, 40, 43** SQA exam rubrics. Copyright © Scottish Qualifications Authority.

Every effort has been made to trace all copyright holders, but if any have been inadvertently overlooked the Publishers will be pleased to make the necessary arrangements at the first opportunity.

Although every effort has been made to ensure that website addresses are correct at time of going to press, Hodder Gibson cannot be held responsible for the content of any website mentioned in this book. It is sometimes possible to find a relocated web page by typing in the address of the home page for a website in the URL window of your browser.

Hachette UK's policy is to use papers that are natural, renewable and recyclable products and made from wood grown in sustainable forests. The logging and manufacturing processes are expected to conform to the environmental regulations of the country of origin.

Orders: please contact Bookpoint Ltd, 130 Park Drive, Milton Park, Abingdon, Oxon OX14 4SE. Telephone: (44) 01235 827720. Fax: (44) 01235 400454. Lines are open 9.00–5.00, Monday to Saturday, with a 24-hour message answering service. Visit our website at www.hoddereducation.co.uk. Hodder Gibson can be contacted direct on: Tel: 0141 333 4650; Fax: 0141 404 8188; email: hoddergibson@hodder.co.uk

# Introduction

## National 5 French

The National 5 French course aims to enable you to develop the ability to read, listen, talk and write in French, that is, to understand and use French, and to apply your knowledge and understanding of the language.

The course offers the opportunity to develop detailed language skills in the real-life contexts of society, learning, employability and culture.

## How the course is graded

The course assessment will take the form of a performance (worth 30 marks) and three question papers (worth 70 marks) through which you will demonstrate your listening, reading and writing skills in French.

- The performance will be a presentation and discussion with your teacher, which will be recorded and marked by your teacher.
- The three question papers will take the form of a written exam that you will sit in May; this book will help you practise for this.

### The exam papers

*Reading and Writing*

- Exam time: 1 hour 30 minutes
- Total marks: 50 (split between Reading: 30 marks and Writing: 20 marks)
- Weighting in final grade: 50%
- What you have to do: read three passages of just under 200 words each, and answer questions about them in English; one of the questions will require you to identify the overall purpose of the text.
- Write 120–150 words in French in the form of an email, applying for a job or work placement: there will be six bullet points for you to address.
- You will be able to use a dictionary throughout this part.

*Listening*

- Exam time: 25 minutes
- Total marks: 20
- Weighting in final grade: 20%
- You will hear two passages; each one three times.
- What you have to do: part 1 – listen to a monologue in French, and answer questions about it in English; part 2 – listen to a short dialogue in French, and answer questions in English.
- The final question in the monologue will ask you to identify the overall purpose of the passage.
- You will not have a dictionary for this part of the exam.

# How to improve your mark!

Every year, examiners notice the same kind of mistakes being made, and they also regularly come across some excellent work. They give advice in the three key areas of reading, listening and writing to help students do better. Here are some key points from their advice.

## Reading

Make sure that your answers include specific details from the Reading paper. Pick out details from longer chunks of language, rather than focusing on individual words. Read the whole passage, then pick out the key points, using the questions as a guide as to where to look. Detailed answers are generally required, so pay particular attention to words like *assez, très, trop, vraiment* and to negatives. Make sure you get the details of numbers, days, times and so on right.

Take care when using dictionaries where a word has more than one meaning. Learn to choose the correct meaning from a list of meanings in a dictionary. Know how verb endings work, as this will help you use your dictionary.

Beware of *faux amis: journée* means 'day', not 'journey'; *appelé* means 'called', not 'appealed'; *histoire* will often mean 'story', for instance!

In responding to the questions in the Reading papers, you should be guided by the number of points awarded for each question. You should give as many details in your answer as you can, as long as you are sure they are correct. However, you should not put down everything in the original text, as you are wasting time. The question itself usually indicates the amount of information required by stating this in bold, for example, 'State (any) **two** things.' Often there are more than two possibilities, but choose the two you are happiest with and stick to them. Don't try to give alternatives, just choose the correct number of responses. It is only worth giving extra answers if you are unsure which answer is correct.

You should re-read your answers to make sure that they make sense and that your English expression is as good as it can be, but you do not have to write in sentences.

## Listening

This is the hardest paper to do well in, and it is the one that improves most with practice. So use the listening items in this book several times, to get used to the format of the exam. Audio files for all the Listening transcripts in this book can be found at www.hoddereducation.co.uk/updatesandextras. The dialogues are particularly worth practising.

Make sure you read the questions carefully before you start to listen, as this will help greatly. Underline key words in the questions before you start, and write notes between the listenings and during the second listening.

Not giving enough detail is still a major reason for candidates losing marks. Many answers are correct as far as they go, but are not sufficiently detailed to score marks. The same rules as for Reading apply.

You hear each of the listening texts three times, so make use of the third listening to check the accuracy and specific details of your answers.

Be sure you are able to give accurate answers through confident knowledge of numbers, common adjectives, weather expressions, prepositions and question words, so that some of the 'easier' points of information are not lost through lack of sufficiently accurate details.

In responding to the questions in the Listening papers, you should be guided by the number of points awarded for each question, and by the wording of the question. You should give as many details in your answer as you can, but you should not write down everything you hear. The question itself usually indicates the amount of information required by marking this in bold, for example, 'State (any) **two** things.' Don't try to give alternatives, just choose the correct number of responses. It is only worth giving extra answers if you are unsure which answer is correct.

Make sure you put a line through any notes you have made.

## Writing

This, along with Talking, is where students do best. Make sure you have some good material prepared and learned, ready to use in the exam.

Where candidates write pieces that are too lengthy, this certainly does not help performance. So stick to writing 20–30 words per bullet point.

There are six bullet points to respond to; most people manage the first four bullet points well, using material they have learned and know is correct. Look at the success criteria (see page 49 in the Answers) and try to model your writing on them. This applies particularly to the last two bullet points in the task, which are a bit more unpredictable.

You should ensure that you are careful when you read the information regarding the job you are applying for, and make sure your answer is tailored to fit that. Depending on the job, you may have to alter your strengths or the experience you are claiming. If it is a job in a café, for instance, your answer should reflect that. Note also that you should be ready to ask questions, as this may well be needed for one of the last two bullet points.

You should be wary of writing long lists of things such as school subjects (and then repeating the list with a past or future verb tense) as part of your answers.

Use the dictionary to check the accuracy of what you have written (spelling, accents, genders, etc.), but not to create new sentences, particularly when dealing with the last two bullet points. You should have everything you need ready prepared when you come into the exam.

Be aware of the extended criteria to be used in assessing performance in Writing, so that you know what is required in terms of content, accuracy and range and variety of language to achieve the 'good' and 'very good' categories.

Ensure that your handwriting is legible (particularly when writing in French) and distinguish clearly between rough notes and what you wish to be considered as final answers. Make sure you score out your notes!

You should bear the following points in mind.

- There are six bullet points to answer: the first four are predictable, the last two vary from year to year.
- Each of the first four bullet points should have between 20 and 30 words to address it properly.
- To get a mark of 'satisfactory' or above, you must address the last two bullet points properly.
- You should aim to have at least 15 words for each of these last two points, but do not try to write too much for these.
- You will be assessed on how well you have answered the points, and on the accuracy of your language.
- For a mark of 'good' or 'very good', you should include some complex language, such as longer, varied sentences and conjunctions.

## How this book will help you

In the answers, you will find two columns on the right-hand side of each page. The first, 'Hint', gives you hints about how you might answer the question better or more easily. The second, 'HTP', gives you page references to the Hodder book *How to Pass National 5 French*. This will provide further advice and improve your chances of answering questions successfully.

# Revision grid

| Revision guide for National 5 French | | |
|---|---|---|
| Reading: Have you ... | answered all the reading questions in this book? | |
| | used the marking schemes to correct them? | |
| | used a dictionary to help you, rather than using a translation programme? | |
| | done the same with past papers and used the SQA marking schemes? (www.sqa.org.uk/pastpapers/findpastpaper.htm) | |
| | checked your timing? 20 minutes per question! | |
| | learned from the introduction the best way to answer a reading paper? | |
| Writing: Have you ... | put together a draft for the first four bullet points? (20–30 words each) | |
| | had this corrected by your teacher? | |
| | put together some alternatives for skills and work experience, ready to match different jobs? | |
| | researched the kind of questions asked in the last two bullet points? (using past papers, and possibly past papers for other languages) | |
| | prepared some questions to ask, if the paper asks you to do this in the last bullet point? | |
| | tried to answer some papers in 30 minutes and had these corrected? | |
| | understood how past tenses work? | |
| | worked out how to use the verb pages in your dictionary? | |
| | looked at the marking schemes to see what you need to do to get a certain grade? (at the back of this book) | |
| Listening: Have you ... | answered all the listening questions in this book? | |
| | used the marking schemes to correct them? | |
| | listened again with the transcript in front of you, to help develop your ear? | |
| | done the same with past papers and used the SQA marking schemes? (www.sqa.org.uk/pastpapers/findpastpaper.htm) | |
| | revised numbers, times, days, months, distances, etc.? | |
| | got into the habit of reading the questions before you listen for the first time? | |
| | listened to exam items again after a couple of months, to see whether you have improved? | |
| | used SCHOLAR to practise your listening? | |
| Talking: Have you ... | put together a presentation which you have had checked by your teacher? | |
| | included a variety of structures and a sense of structure in it? | |
| | worked out the best way to have notes which will support you when you deliver the presentation? (40 words, plus some illustrations if that helps!) | |
| | recorded it and listened back? | |
| | put together a list of possible questions you might be asked? | |
| | thought about answers to these questions? | |
| | put together some questions of your own? | |
| | looked at the criteria used to mark your conversation? | |
| | prepared some language to give you time to think? (phrases like *un moment*, which allow you to hesitate) | |
| | thought hard about vocabulary for giving your opinion? (positive and negative) | |
| | prepared another topic area in case you run out of things to say? | |

# National 5
# French

HODDER
GIBSON
LEARN MORE

# Reading

## Item 1

You find this article about a burglary gone wrong. (Culture)

**Les cambrioleurs appellent la police !**

Réveillé très tôt le matin ce mardi par l'alarme de sa pizzeria, située à une centaine de mètres de l'appartement qu'il habitait, le propriétaire est allé immédiatement sur place. « J'ai mis un t-shirt, un pantalon et des chaussures et j'ai couru à ma pizzeria », a-t-il dit au journal local. Mais les cambrioleurs ont préféré être arrêtés par la police plutôt que de tomber entre les mains du restaurateur qu'ils étaient en train de cambrioler.

Sur place, il a trouvé quatre personnes, qui prenaient son argent et des équipements. Il y a eu une dispute violente, et les voleurs ont refusé de rendre ses biens au restaurateur. L'un des cambrioleurs s'est caché dans les toilettes parce qu'il se sentait gravement menacé par la victime. Là, il a téléphoné à la police, qui est arrivée rapidement. « La police a sauvé deux hommes de dix-huit et dix-neuf ans de la fureur du propriétaire et les a arrêtés », a annoncé le porte-parole de la police. Quant aux deux autres cambrioleurs, ils ont réussi à s'enfuir et n'ont pas été identifiés.

Selon le patron de la pizzeria, interrogé par la presse locale, c'est la troisième tentative de cambriolage qu'il subit en deux ans. « Enfin, j'étais en colère », a-t-il dit.

*Based on an article in* Le Parisien.

# A

## Questions

a) (i) What woke the owner of the shop up?

_____

1

   (ii) Where exactly was his business?

_____

1

b) What did he do immediately? Give details.

_____

_____

2

c) What did he find when he reached his business? State **two** things.

_____

_____

2

d) (i) What did one of the burglars do? Give details.

_____

_____

2

   (ii) Why did he do this?

_____

1

e) What happened to two of the burglars? Tick (✓) the correct statement.

1

| | |
|---|---|
| They fled and have not been identified. | |
| They were furious with the police. | |
| They have tried to break into the pizzeria three times in the last two years. | |

# Item 2

You read an article about a brave young boy. (Society)

**Un petit garçon sauve son père à vélo**

Mercredi soir, un père fait une crise cardiaque, alors qu'il est avec ses deux jeunes enfants, à la maison. Son fils, un petit garçon de cinq ans, a pris son vélo pour alerter sa mère. Vers 22h30 du soir, un automobiliste voit sur une route de campagne un petit garçon en vélo habillé d'un pyjama et très froid sous la pluie. « Je rentrais chez moi, sur la route N5 », explique l'automobiliste. Il s'arrête. Là, le garçon lui annonce: « Mon papa est mort. »

Le petit garçon explique alors au chauffeur qu'il est parti de chez lui pour aller chercher sa maman qui travaille de nuit dans une usine. Le chauffeur appelle alors la gendarmerie. Lorsque les gendarmes arrivent, les paroles de l'enfant sont confuses. « C'est normal à son âge. C'était difficile de déterminer exactement où il habitait, et aussi où était sa maman. » Rapidement, ils essaient de retrouver sa maison. En moins d'une demi-heure, les secours arrivent chez lui. Ils retrouvent le père de famille, par terre et inconscient. Transporté à l'hôpital, l'homme est sauvé.

« Ce petit garçon est incroyable ! Ce qu'il a fait est très intelligent. Sa mère m'a appelé pour me remercier et me dire que son époux était sorti de l'hôpital », raconte l'automobiliste.

*Based on articles in* Le Parisien *and* Ouest-France.

# Questions

**MARKS**

**a)** What had happened to the boy's father?

1

**b)** Which of the following statements is true, according to the article?
Tick (✓) the correct statement.

1

| | |
|---|---|
| The young boy and his mum set off on bikes. | |
| Two young children left their home to find help. | |
| The young boy set off to warn his mother. | |

**c)** **(i)** When exactly did the motorist find the boy? Give details.

2

**(ii)** What condition was the boy in? State any **one** thing.

1

MARKS

**d)** What did the boy say to the motorist to explain why he was there?
He had left home to find ... who was ...

2

_____

_____

**e)** How long did it take the police to find the boy's father?

1

_____

**f)** Why did the boy's mother phone the car driver? Give **two** reasons.

2

_____

_____

# Item 3

You are given this leaflet, encouraging people to learn a language. (Learning)

---

**Comment apprendre une nouvelle langue ?**

Lorsque l'on se lance dans l'apprentissage d'une nouvelle langue, on est toujours enthousiaste. Cet enthousiasme est un élément positif, mais ne comptez pas uniquement sur lui. Allez doucement : l'apprentissage de la langue doit devenir une activité régulière. Mieux vaut dix minutes par jour qu'une semaine intense et après … plus rien.

Beaucoup pensent qu'apprendre par cœur est la solution à tout : une bonne mémoire est certainement utile, apprendre des phrases par cœur peut être utile dans certaines situations mais cela ne vous aidera pas si le sujet de conversation est nouveau.

Un des problèmes avec la « maîtrise » d'une langue est le désir absurde d'avoir une prononciation et une grammaire parfaites. C'est possible avec beaucoup d'entraînement, mais cela ne devrait pas être votre priorité si vous commencez à apprendre une nouvelle langue. Donc courage, et n'ayez pas peur de faire des erreurs.

Vous apprenez régulièrement, vous utilisez bien votre mémoire, vous avez compris que l'on apprend de ses erreurs et vous avez commencé à pratiquer … et maintenant ? Désormais, il est temps de faire quelque chose d'amusant. Regardez un film, chantez une chanson, écoutez la radio … Mais dans la langue que vous apprenez, bien entendu !

---

## Questions

MARKS

**a)** What does the leaflet say is the normal feeling when you start to learn a language?

1

_____

**b)** What is the first piece of advice given? State any **two** things.

2

_____

_____

**c) (i)** What do many people think is the answer to learning a language?

1

_____

**(ii)** What could be the problem with this approach?

1

_____

**d) (i)** What does the leaflet say is absurd about 'mastering' a language. State **two** things.

2

_____

_____

MARKS

**(ii)** What should you do instead, according to the leaflet?
State any **two** things.

2

_____

_____

**e)** What is the leaflet's overall purpose in discussing learning a language?
Tick (✓) the correct statement.

1

| | |
|---|---|
| It is telling you learning a language is easy. | |
| It is trying to get people to be realistic about language learning. | |
| It is trying to get you to sign up to a course with the company. | |

**(End of Reading paper)**

# Writing

You are preparing an application for the job advertised below and you write an email in **French** to the company.

Le grand magasin, « Zara » à Paris offre des emplois saisonniers cet été.

Il nous faut des employés qui sont surtout prêts à travailler le soir et le weekend.

Si cette offre d'emploi vous intéresse, veuillez communiquer par email avec vos coordonnées à : info/fr@zara.com

To help you to write your email, you have been given the following checklist of information to give about yourself and to ask about the job.

You must include all of these points:

- personal details (name, age, where you live)
- school/college/education experience until now
- skills/interests you have which make you right for the job
- related work experience
- a request for information about the days and hours you would be expected to work
- your reasons for wanting to work in Paris.

Use all of the above to help you write the email in **French**. The email should be approximately 120–150 words. You may use a French dictionary.

**(End of Writing paper)**

# Listening

## Item 1

Listen to this radio report about a new agreement between the clothing store Zara and its unions. (Employability)

### Questions

MARKS

**a)** What will the agreement allow?

1

_____

**b)** The report gives details of new arrangements for pay and conditions.

    **(i)** In what way will it affect the pay of people who work at Zara?
State any **one** thing.

1

    _____

    **(ii)** Apart from salary, there are other perks mentioned. Give details
of **two** of these.

2

    _____

    _____

**c)** When will the store have to close at night in summer?

1

_____

**d)** How many stores are involved in these new arrangements?

1

_____

**e)** If a store cannot find enough employees to open, there are two possibilities mentioned. Give details of **one** of them.

1

_____

**f)** What is the overall attitude of the report? Tick (✓) the correct statement.

1

| | |
|---|---|
| The reporter is stunned at how well people will be paid. | |
| The reporter is against Sunday working. | |
| The reporter is giving a neutral report of what has been agreed. | |

# A

## Item 2

Alain talks to Caroline about her opinions on working in the evenings and on Sundays.
(Employability)

### Questions

MARKS

**a)** Alain asks Caroline if she is tired after working the previous evening.

  **(i)** How does she feel?

  1

  **(ii)** She explains her reasons for working. Give details.

  2

**b)** He asks her how she feels about working on Sundays.

  She gives several reasons for being positive about this. State any **two** of them.

  2

**c)** Caroline says most other employees feel positive about Sunday working. Give any **two** reasons why this might be the case.

  2

**d)** Caroline mentions the economic crisis.

  **(i)** What does she think this should mean?

  1

  **(ii)** What example of her own does she give?

  1

**e)** She gives reasons why one of her colleagues is not happy working on Sundays. State any **one** of them.

  1

MARKS

**f)** Caroline mentions a risk for employees with evening and Sunday working. What is this?

1

_____

**g)** She tells Alain what a Japanese client had said to her. What was her opinion? Tick (✓) the correct statement.

1

| | |
|---|---|
| She has a shop herself and it is always closed on Sundays. | |
| In a city like Paris, shops should be open every day. | |
| In Paris she finds the shops are all open every day anyway. | |

**(End of Listening paper)**

# Listening transcript

> **Instructions to reader(s)**
>
> For each item, read the English **once**, then read the French **three times**, with an interval of one minute between the three readings. On completion of the third reading, pause for the length of time indicated in brackets after the item, to allow the candidates to write their answers.
>
> Where special arrangements have been agreed in advance to allow the reading of the material, those sections marked **(f)** should be read by a female speaker and those marked **(m)** by a male; those sections marked **(t)** should be read by the teacher.

# Item 1

---

> **(t)** **Item Number One**
>
> Listen to this radio report about a new agreement between the clothing store Zara and its unions.
>
> **You now have one minute to study the questions for Item Number One.**
>
> **(m)** Cette année, les magasins Zara situés à Paris vont ouvrir leurs portes les dimanches. Zara et les syndicats ont signé mardi un accord qui le permet.
>
> Les employés vont recevoir un supplément de salaire de 110 % les dimanches et un salaire double le soir. Zara va aussi payer les frais de garde des enfants, pour les employés qui ont des enfants et, en plus, le retour en taxi des employés qui ne peuvent pas prendre les transports en commun pour rentrer le soir. Les heures de service dans ces boutiques vont être limitées à 21 heures 30 l'hiver et à 22 heures l'été.
>
> Au total, une trentaine de magasins de Paris sont concernés par cet accord. 90 % des employés ont répondu favorablement au travail le dimanche et 70 % au travail le soir.
>
> En plus, Zara s'est engagé à respecter le principe du volontariat. S'il n'y a pas assez d'employés prêts à travailler le dimanche ou le soir, il y a deux possibilités : un magasin peut ne pas ouvrir ou le magasin peut faire appel à des employés d'un autre magasin dans la même zone géographique.
>
> *(2 minutes)*

# Item 2

Alain talks to Caroline about her opinions on working in the evenings and on Sundays.

**You now have one minute to study the questions for Item Number Two.**

**(m)** Salut, Caroline, ça va ? Tu n'es pas trop fatiguée après avoir travaillé hier soir ?

**(f)** Non, je ne suis pas du tout fatiguée ; et puis c'était une bonne opportunité de gagner plus : 300 € nets supplémentaires, à raison de quatre soirs cette semaine.

**(m)** Donc, tu es contente de travailler le soir. Mais que penses-tu du travail le dimanche ?

**(f)** Les conditions de travail sont beaucoup plus agréables les dimanches, les gens sont plus détendus qu'en semaine. Ils se contentent de flâner, de partager un moment avec nous.

**(m)** Les autres employés pensent comme toi ?

**(f)** En fait, la plupart des gens sont favorables au travail le dimanche s'il y a de bons arguments financiers. L'ouverture des magasins le dimanche offre des emplois. Et puis les habitudes ont changé. Les Parisiens ne se retrouvent plus forcément autour du traditionnel repas de famille dominical.

**(m)** Pourquoi est-ce qu'ils pensent comme ça ?

**(f)** C'est une réponse à la crise économique. Avec la crise, il faut laisser travailler les gens qui veulent travailler. Lorsque j'ai travaillé au magasin sur les Champs-Élysées le dimanche, j'étais contente car j'ai gagné le triple de mon salaire normal.

**(m)** Alors, tout le monde pense ainsi ?

**(f)** Non, j'ai une collègue qui veut passer ce jour-là en famille. Elle a trois jeunes enfants. Elle dit qu'il y a déjà beaucoup de magasins ouverts les dimanches. Il faut préserver la vie familiale.

**(m)** Donc tu es très positive vis-à-vis du travail les dimanches ?

**(f)** Oui, mais je sais qu'il y a un risque que des pressions soient exercées sur les employés qui refuseraient de travailler les dimanches.

**(m)** Et les clients, qu'est-ce qu'ils en disent ?

**(f)** Eh bien, une Italienne m'a dit qu'elle a une boutique à Milan et qu'elle ferme le dimanche. Mais une Japonaise m'a dit que, dans une capitale comme Paris, les magasins doivent être ouverts tous les jours.

**(m)** Alors, si je veux te voir dimanche, il faut que je te rende visite au magasin ?

**(f)** Oui, et tu peux toujours venir m'acheter un cadeau !

*(2 minutes)*

**(t)** **End of test.**

**Now look over your answers.**

**(End of transcript)**

# National 5 French

# Reading

**Total marks:** 30

Attempt ALL questions.

Write your answers clearly, in **English**, in the spaces provided in this booklet.

You may use a French dictionary.

Additional space for answers is provided at the end of this booklet. If you use this space you must clearly identify the question number you are attempting.

Use **blue** or **black** ink.

There is a separate question and answer booklet for Writing. You must complete your answer for Writing in the question and answer booklet for Writing.

Before leaving the examination room you must give both booklets to the Invigilator; if you do not, you may lose all the marks for this paper.

# Item 1

You read this article written for new students at university. (Society)

### Quels sont les besoins nutritionnels d'un étudiant ?

Cela dépend. Pour un adulte, ils sont de 2 400 calories par jour pour les hommes, 1 800 pour les femmes. Vous avez besoin de quelques calories de plus si vous pratiquez une activité sportive. Trois à quatre repas étalés sur la journée sont nécessaires pour le bon fonctionnement du corps – notamment du cerveau. Toute journée doit commencer par un petit déjeuner. Le déjeuner et le dîner doivent contenir une source de protéines, des légumes, un laitage et / ou un fruit.

À midi, l'idéal est le restaurant universitaire. Pour un prix modeste, on peut y prendre un repas équilibré. En entrée, il faut choisir des crudités ou un demi-pamplemousse pour les vitamines et les fibres. Ensuite, un morceau de viande ou de poisson accompagné de légumes et des pâtes ou du riz. Enfin, un fruit.

On doit éviter la restauration rapide. Hamburgers, pizzas, paninis et kebabs sont gras et nutritionnellement peu intéressants. On peut y manger une fois par semaine, au plus. L'idéal est d'acheter un sandwich simple (jambon, poulet, thon) ou une quiche aux légumes ou des sushis, par exemple, et de compléter avec des tomates cerises, un yaourt et une pomme.

## Questions

**a)** **(i)** What might cause you to need more calories to be healthy?

_____

1

**(ii)** Why should you have three or four meals over the course of a day, according to the article?

_____

1

**b)** The article tells us what the main meals should consist of. Complete the sentence.

Lunch and dinner should contain a ..., some ..., a dairy product and a piece of fruit.

_____

_____

2

**c)** The writer recommends the university canteen to students.

**(i)** Why does he do so? State **two** things.

_____

_____

2

**(ii)** Why does he recommend raw vegetables or a half-grapefruit as a starter? Give details.

_____

1

**d)** The writer discusses eating in fast food restaurants.

**(i)** Why does the writer not recommend them? State any **one** reason.

_____

1

**(ii)** What other piece of advice does the writer give about fast food restaurants?

_____

1

**e)** What is the writer's overall purpose in discussing diet? Tick (✓) the correct statement.

1

| To encourage people only to eat in the university canteen. | |
| To stop people eating junk food. | |
| To encourage students to eat healthily. | |

# Item 2

You read this set of advice for French students preparing to revise for an exam. (Learning)

Commencez par faire un plan. Matière par matière, listez les sujets à réviser, notez vos points forts et vos points faibles, listez les questions à poser aux professeurs. Faites un planning à la semaine et à la journée. Attention, fixez-vous des objectifs concrets et raisonnables. Ne vous mettez pas trop de pression, vous risquez de vous décourager.

Nous n'avons pas tous la même façon d'apprendre et les livres ne sont pas le seul moyen de faire travailler sa mémoire. Pour ceux qui ont une mémoire auditive, soyez attentifs et participez en cours, cela vous aidera beaucoup. Relisez vos cours à voix haute et organisez des sessions de révisions avec vos amis. Enfin, pour ceux qui ont une mémoire visuelle, faites des croquis*, utilisez des couleurs pour relire vos cours, complétez vos notes avec vos commentaires.

Attention à votre santé, vous aurez besoin de toutes vos forces pour ces prochaines semaines. Dormez suffisamment et couchez-vous à des heures régulières. Ne sautez pas de repas et mangez équilibré. Enfin, faites du sport pour vous aérer. Votre corps et votre cerveau en ont besoin.

Travaillez dans de bonnes conditions. Alors éteignez votre portable, l'ordinateur, la télé ... et concentrez-vous. Vous ne supportez pas le silence ? Vous pouvez travailler avec un fond musical : cela vous aidera à vous concentrer.

*croquis : sketch, (here) mindmap

## Questions

**MARKS**

**a)** The article tells you to start with a plan. What should you note down? State any **two** things.

2

_____

_____

**b)** Which of the following statements are true, according to the article? Tick (✓) the **two** correct statements.

2

| Don't take on too much, you might be discouraged. | |
|---|---|
| We learn differently at different times. | |
| Using books is not the best way to improve your memory. | |
| If you have an auditory memory, taking part in lessons is beneficial. | |

**c)** The article gives ideas for those who have a visual memory. Give details.

2

_____

_____

MARKS

**d)** The article goes on to give information about the importance of your health.

    **(i)** What is the first thing you are told to do?

    1

_____

    **(ii)** Some other important advice is given. State any **one** thing.

    1

_____

**e)** The article closes with some advice about working conditions.

    **(i)** What should you switch off? State any **one** thing.

    1

_____

    **(ii)** What might help some people concentrate?

    1

_____

# Item 3

You read this article about a French teenager who has been volunteering in the USA. (Culture)

> En août dernier, à l'âge de dix-sept ans, Sylvain n'a pas hésité à traverser l'Atlantique. « J'ai toujours eu envie de partir à l'étranger pour pratiquer l'anglais. Mais je ne savais pas comment. »
>
> Pas facile de partir seul à l'étranger quand on n'a pas encore dix-huit ans et peu d'argent en poche. Donc le jeune homme choisit la solution de chantier volontaire international, tous frais payés, dans le Vermont, dans le nord-est des États-Unis, pour quatre semaines de travail. Sur place, il découvre la mission qu'il va remplir avec douze autres jeunes, venus de divers pays d'Europe et des quatre coins des États-Unis.
>
> Entretien d'un parc, construction d'une cabane ... chaque jour, ils travaillent jusqu'en début d'après-midi. Puis après l'effort, ils visitent la région et parlent anglais ensemble. Pour Sylvain, pas question de rester dans son coin à cause de la barrière de la langue. « Après ces quelques semaines, j'ai bien amélioré mon anglais, même si je suis encore loin de le maîtriser ! »
>
> Les progrès sont encourageants pour Sylvain qui, avant, était un élève « très moyen » dans cette matière. Sylvain a gardé le contact avec les autres participants à ce séjour. Facebook, Skype ... tous les moyens sont bons pour entretenir ces liens d'amitié et garder un bon niveau en anglais.

# Questions

**MARKS**

**a)** How old was Sylvain when he went to the United States?

1

**b)** Why did he want to go there?

1

**c)** He talks about working on a voluntary project.

   **(i)** What made him choose to do so?

1

   **(ii)** How long did his placement last for?

1

   **(ii)** Where did other participants come from? Give details.

2

MARKS

**d)** Which of the following statements is true, according to the article?
Tick (✓) the **two** correct statements.

2

| They looked after a park and built a hut. | |
|---|---|
| They only worked in the afternoons. | |
| Not everyone could speak English. | |
| The four weeks really improved his English. | |

**e)** Sylvain talks about what the experience has done for him.

**(i)** What does he say about his level of English prior to the trip?

1

_____

**(ii)** What does using social media mean for him now? State any **one** thing.

1

_____

**(End of Reading paper)**

# Writing

You are preparing an application for the job advertised below and you write an email in **French** to the company.

---

**Hôtel Royal Cannes**

Cherche un réceptionniste

Nous cherchons une jeune personne qui pourra travailler les weekends dans notre hôtel à Cannes. Vous devrez aussi être prêt à travailler tard les soirs.

Nous préférons quelqu'un qui parle aussi l'anglais, car beaucoup de nos clients ne parlent pas français. Nous offrons aussi la possibilité d'une chambre.

Si cette offre d'emploi vous intéresse, veuillez communiquer par email avec vos coordonnées à : reception@royalcannes.fr

---

To help you to write your email, you have been given the following checklist of information to give about yourself and to ask about the job.

You must include all of these points:

- personal details (name, age, where you live)
- school/college/education experience until now
- skills/interests you have which make you right for the job
- related work experience
- a request for information about the days and hours you would be expected to work
- whether you would wish to take up the offer of accommodation.

Use all of the above to help you write the email in **French**. The email should be approximately 120–150 words. You may use a French dictionary.

**(End of Writing paper)**

# Listening

**Total marks:** 20

Attempt ALL questions.

You will hear two items in French. **Before you hear each item, you will have one minute to study the questions.** You will hear each item three times, with an interval of one minute between playings. You will then have time to answer the questions before hearing the next item.

You may NOT use a French dictionary.

Write your answers clearly, in **English**, in the spaces provided in this booklet. Additional space for answers is provided at the end of this booklet. If you use this space you must clearly identify the question number you are attempting.

Use **blue** or **black** ink.

You are not allowed to leave the examination room until the end of the test.

Before leaving the examination room you must give this booklet to the Invigilator; if you do not, you may lose all the marks for this paper.

# Item 1

You listen to this radio programme for young people looking for a training place in college after school. (Employability)

## Questions

MARKS

**a)** Who might you talk to for information?

1

_____

**b)** The report gives details of other ways of finding information.

   **(i)** What might you do if you have an idea of the job you are interested in?

1

   _____

   **(ii)** What should you do when you find something that interests you?

1

   _____

c)   The speaker explains what happens if a college accepts your application.

   (i)   What will the college do first?

   _____

1

   (ii)   State **one** thing you might be asked for.

   _____

1

   (iii)   By which date should you do this?

   _____

1

d)   Why should you not panic if you have not heard anything by the end of May?

   _____

1

e)   What is the overall attitude of the report? Tick (✓) the correct statement.

1

| | |
|---|---|
| It is explaining that it is very difficult to find a training place nowadays. | |
| It is explaining the steps a young person in the last year of school should take. | |
| It is discussing whether pupils should look for a training place or start work right away. | |

# B

## Item 2

You listen to an interview between Alain and Mathilde, a young French woman who has completed her training as an electrician. (Employability)

## Questions

|  |  | MARKS |
|---|---|---|

**a)** Alain asks Mathilde if this was the career she always wanted.

    **(i)** What field did she first work in? — **1**

    _____

    **(ii)** What reason does she give for moving on from this? — **1**

    _____

**b)** He asks her what made her choose this profession.

    **(i)** What was the direct cause of her choosing to be an electrician? Give details. — **1**

    _____

    **(ii)** When did she actually start her new career? — **1**

    _____

**c)** Mathilde talks about how it was difficult at first. Give any **one** reason why this was the case. — **1**

_____

**d)** Mathilde describes her training. Complete the sentence.

The training lasted for ..., then I spent a year working for Jean-Claude, before ... — **2**

_____

_____

**e)** She describes her working day. Give details of how this works. — **2**

_____

_____

**f)** Alain talks about the problems that might arise from her working in 'a flowery blouse and boots'. Mathilde mentions several people she gets on well with. Tick (✓) the **two** correct items. — **2**

| | |
|---|---|
| Plumber | |
| Electrician | |
| Plasterer | |
| Joiner | |

**g)** How does she find new customers? — **1**

_____

**(End of Listening paper)**

# Listening transcript

## Item 1

**(t)   Item Number One**

You listen to this radio programme for young people looking for a training place in college after school.

**You now have one minute to study the questions for Item Number One.**

**(f)**   D'abord, prenez le temps de trouver des informations sur vos possibilités. Cherchez des informations et des renseignements chez vos professeurs et vos conseillers d'orientation. Si vous avez une idée de la formation que vous voulez suivre, allez aux journées portes ouvertes, pour trouver beaucoup d'infos ! Vous pouvez aussi consulter les informations publiées par les établissements qui offrent une formation. Puis, déposez votre candidature pour les formations qui vous intéressent.

Si un établissement accepte votre candidature, vous allez recevoir une offre par lettre ou par email. Certains établissements demandent des documents comme votre CV, votre bulletin scolaire, etc. sous forme électronique ou sur papier. N'oubliez pas d'envoyer les papiers demandés. Vous avez jusqu'au 2 avril pour envoyer les papiers.

Finalement, c'est la phase la plus importante. Quand vous recevez une proposition d'un établissement, vous avez quatre jours pour répondre. Si vous n'avez pas reçu de proposition avant fin mai, ne paniquez pas. Il y a une session supplémentaire mise en place à partir du 24 juin. Elle propose les places restées vacantes.

*(2 minutes)*

# B

## Item 2

**(t) Item Number Two**

You listen to an interview between Alain and Mathilde, a young French woman who has completed her training as an electrician.

**You now have one minute to study the questions for Item Number Two.**

**(m)** Salut Mathilde, tu es électricienne maintenant. Tu as toujours voulu être électricienne ?

**(f)** Non, j'ai commencé dans l'agriculture. Mais avec les animaux que j'avais, je ne gagnais pas assez pour vivre. Maintenant je garde quand même mes animaux !

**(m)** Pourquoi donc as-tu voulu être électricienne ?

**(f)** Je suis devenue électricienne parce que je n'avais plus d'électricité dans ma salle de bains. J'ai pensé : « Et si j'apprenais l'électricité ? » C'était il y a quatre ans et j'ai fait un stage chez Jean-Claude, l'électricien du coin.

**(m)** Comment était-il ?

**(f)** Je m'entendais bien avec lui.

**(m)** Comment s'est passé la formation ?

**(f)** D'abord, je l'ai trouvée dure. J'étais la seule femme dans la formation, et quelques-uns des autres apprentis pensaient que je ne devais pas être là. Mais j'ai trouvé intéressant de faire des choses comme, par exemple, décider de l'emplacement des appareils électriques, les prises, les interrupteurs, tout ça. Au bout d'un certain temps, les autres m'ont acceptée.

**(m)** Combien de temps a duré la formation ?

**(f)** La formation a duré trois ans et, après, je suis restée un an chez Jean-Claude, avant de travailler pour moi-même.

**(m)** Comment est-ce que tu trouves le travail à ton compte ?

**(f)** C'est beaucoup mieux. Je travaille aux heures qui me conviennent – normalement l'après-midi pour profiter des matinées avec mes animaux, avant de faire quelques heures comme électricienne.

**(m)** Mathilde, tu exerces un métier occupé par des hommes, en chemise à fleurs et avec des bottes. Qu'est-ce que tu penses de ça ?

**(f)** Par exemple, je travaille cette semaine dans une maison en rénovation près de chez moi. Je connais les gens qui y travaillent comme le plombier, le constructeur et le menuisier. Nous nous entendons bien, donc pas de problème !

**(m)** Comment est-ce que tu trouves tes clients ?

**(f)** Je trouve mes clients par le bouche-à-oreille, des amis d'amis qui me recommandent. J'ai une bonne réputation, donc je trouve toujours de nouveaux clients.

**(m)** Merci d'avoir répondu à mes questions, Mathilde !

**(f)** De rien.

*(2 minutes)*

**(t) End of test.**

**Now look over your answers.**

(End of transcript)

# National 5
# French

# Reading

**Total marks:** 30

Attempt ALL questions.

Write your answers clearly, in **English**, in the spaces provided in this booklet.

You may use a French dictionary.

Additional space for answers is provided at the end of this booklet. If you use this space you must clearly identify the question number you are attempting.

Use **blue** or **black** ink.

There is a separate question and answer booklet for Writing. You must complete your answer for Writing in the question and answer booklet for Writing.

Before leaving the examination room you must give both booklets to the Invigilator; if you do not, you may lose all the marks for this paper.

# Item 1

You read this article discussing the importance of breakfast. (Society)

Il faut prendre un petit-déjeuner pour être plus actif le matin. Surtout en cas de surpoids ou d'obésité, prendre un petit-déjeuner favorise une plus grande activité physique le matin, et permet donc de lutter contre une tendance à rester sédentaire.

Le petit-déjeuner comprend idéalement une boisson, chaude ou froide et des féculents* : c'est-à-dire des produits céréaliers, de préférence de nature complexe comme des céréales ou du pain complet pour l'énergie, du lait ou un yaourt pour le calcium et les protéines, et un fruit, le premier des cinq fruits ou légumes de la journée.

Pour nos enfants, le petit-déjeuner peut être le repas le plus important de la journée. Prendre un petit-déjeuner permet aux élèves d'avoir de meilleures notes à l'école. On a établi un lien entre la prise du petit-déjeuner et les résultats scolaires. Les élèves qui mangent un bon petit-déjeuner le matin ont deux fois plus de chances de dépasser la moyenne que les autres.

La qualité du petit-déjeuner a aussi été identifiée comme importante : ceux qui consomment au réveil des bonbons, chips, les boissons gazeuses et autres aliments moins sains ne vont pas voir leurs notes s'améliorer.

*féculents : carbohydrates

# C

## Questions

**a)** **(i)** Why should you eat breakfast in the morning, according to the article?

1

_____

**(ii)** Who might be particularly helped by this?

1

_____

**(iii)** Why is this the case?

1

_____

**b)** Which of these items should feature in a healthy breakfast? Tick (✓) the **two** correct boxes.

2

| | |
|---|---|
| A hot or cold drink | |
| White bread for energy | |
| A yoghurt | |
| Five pieces of fruit | |

**c)** The article goes on to discuss the importance of a good breakfast for children.

**(i)** What might a good breakfast do for children?

1

_____

**(ii)** What evidence are we given of this? Give details.

2

_____

_____

**d)** The writer tells us that the quality of breakfast is also important, and mentions several foods which do not help. State any **two** of them.

2

_____

_____

# Item 2

You read this article about smoking in schools in France. (Learning)

Les lycées demandent la permission de laisser les élèves fumer dans leurs établissements pour éviter que leurs élèves sortent à l'extérieur des bâtiments en période de risque terroriste. À la suite des attentats du 13 novembre 2015, le gouvernement français a décrété l'état d'urgence ; ce qui affecte les écoles et, en plus, certains lycées ont récemment été l'objet de menaces.

Donc les directeurs ou proviseurs* demandent une nouvelle mesure de sécurité : ils veulent que les élèves puissent fumer dans la cour et non pas dans la rue pendant les récrés et les pauses. Les règles du ministère de l'Éducation nationale rendent cette demande impossible. Laisser les élèves fumer à l'intérieur est interdit.

Mais la sécurité des élèves doit être organisée de la meilleure façon possible, donc on propose des zones fumeurs dans les cours de récréation. Les chefs d'établissements ont demandé cette semaine au Premier ministre de permettre aux élèves de fumer dans leurs écoles.

Pour le moment, la direction générale de la santé a refusé cette autorisation, car elle pense que l'état d'urgence ne change rien à la situation. Pourtant, parce que certains directeurs ou proviseurs considèrent la sécurité des élèves comme plus importante que les règles, ils ont déjà pris l'initiative d'organiser des zones fumeurs dans leurs cours de récréation.

*proviseurs : head teachers

*Based on an article in* Ouest-France.

# Questions

MARKS

**a)** The article tells us schools are asking permission for their pupils to be able to smoke while at school. Why are they doing this? Give details.

2

_____

_____

**b)** What has happened to some schools recently?

1

_____

**c)** Head teachers in some schools have been seeking additional security measures. Complete the sentence.

They want their pupils to be able to ... and not in the street at ...

2

_____

_____

MARKS

**d)** Why is this not possible just now?

1

_____

**e)** **(i)** To help organise things safely for pupils, what exactly is being proposed?

1

_____

**(ii)** What has been the response of the Health Ministry?

1

_____

**f)** The article closes with news of what some head teachers have done.

**(i)** Why have they done this?

1

_____

**(ii)** What exactly have they done?

1

_____

# Item 3

You read this article about a young French woman who took part in a voluntary project. (Employability)

---

À la fin de ses études en 2013, Morgane Vairaa, de Mulsanne, a décidé de s'engager pour un Service Volontaire Européen. Elle avait fini ses études d'économie internationale et est partie dix mois, en Arménie. Elle devait s'occuper d'une centaine d'enfants en difficulté, de six à seize ans, dans un centre social à Erevan, la capitale de l'Arménie.

« Au début, j'avais un peu de mal à cause de la langue, mais j'avais une traductrice anglaise. Petit à petit, j'ai appris la langue et j'ai été très vite intégrée », reconnaît Morgane. « D'ailleurs, je me suis fait des amis et j'y retournerai, car les Arméniens sont très hospitaliers. »

Comment a-t-elle trouvé le pays? « L'Arménie a des difficultés économiques et politiques. Mais on sent que les jeunes veulent réussir. » Elle décrit un pays montagneux et très beau, avec des changements à chaque saison. « Très tranquille, aussi, et je faisais de l'auto-stop sans problème. »

Morgane a beaucoup appris de son volontariat européen. « Mais surtout, j'ai obtenu un poste comme agent administratif au gouvernement pour le plan "Migrants". » Dans quinze jours, elle ira à Metz pour prendre son nouveau poste.

*Based on an article in* Ouest-France.

## Questions

MARKS

**a)** How long did Morgane go to Armenia for?　1

**b)** What was her role? State any **two** things.　2

**c)** She talks about the difficulties she had at first.

(i) What was her first problem?　1

(ii) What was the long-term solution to this problem?　1

**d)** Morgane makes several statements about Armenia. Give details of any **two** things she says.　2

# C

**e)** What has the result of the visit been for Morgane? State any **two** things.

_____

_____

**f)** What is Morgane's overall feeling about her experience? Tick (✓) the correct statement.

| | |
|---|---|
| She found it was very difficult to carry out her role. | |
| She was not very keen on Armenia, as it was so poor. | |
| She enjoyed her experience and learned a lot from it. | |

**(End of Reading paper)**

# Writing

You are preparing an application for the job advertised below and you write an email in **French** to the company.

---

**FNAC**

Cherche vendeurs pour les rayons de musique et de film

Nous cherchons pour le mois de décembre de jeunes personnes pour notre filiale à Lille. Vous devrez aussi être prêt à travailler le weekend.

Nous préférons quelqu'un qui parle aussi l'anglais, car beaucoup de nos clients arrivent en Eurostar ou par l'Eurotunnel.

Si cette offre d'emploi vous intéresse, veuillez communiquer par email avec vos coordonnées à : info@fnaclille.fr

---

To help you to write your email, you have been given the following checklist of information to give about yourself and to ask about the job.

You must include all of these points:

- personal details (name, age, where you live)
- school/college/education experience until now
- skills/interests you have which make you right for the job
- related work experience
- a request for information about the hours you would be expected to work
- details of your interest in films and/or music.

Use all of the above to help you write the email in **French**. The email should be approximately 120–150 words. You may use a French dictionary.

**(End of Writing paper)**

# Listening

> **Total marks:** 20
>
> Attempt ALL questions.
>
> You will hear two items in French. **Before you hear each item, you will have one minute to study the questions.** You will hear each item three times, with an interval of one minute between playings. You will then have time to answer the questions before hearing the next item.
>
> You may NOT use a French dictionary.
>
> Write your answers clearly, in **English**, in the spaces provided in this booklet. Additional space for answers is provided at the end of this booklet. If you use this space you must clearly identify the question number you are attempting.
>
> Use **blue** or **black** ink.
>
> You are not allowed to leave the examination room until the end of the test.
>
> Before leaving the examination room you must give this booklet to the Invigilator; if you do not, you may lose all the marks for this paper.

## Item 1

You listen to this radio programme about going abroad for a holiday job. (Culture)

### Questions

| | MARKS |
|---|---|

**a)** The programme begins with some important advice on what to think about first.

    **(i)** What is the first thing you should know?

       1

    **(ii)** The report mentions some jobs where this might be less important. State any **one** of them.

       1

**b)** The report goes on to talk about practical things you need to know. What do you need to have before travelling in Europe? State **one** thing.

       1

**c)** The speaker describes a special visa programme available in certain countries such as Canada, Australia and New Zealand.

    **(i)** How long is the visa valid for?

       1

    **(ii)** What does it allow you to do?

       1

MARKS

**(iii)** What else must you have? State **one** thing.

1

**d)** The speaker advises going to a youth information centre. What help might you get there? State **one** thing.

1

**e)** What is the overall purpose of the report? Tick (✓) the correct statement.

1

| | |
|---|---|
| It is giving clear advice to help young people find work abroad. | |
| It is warning that this is not a step to take lightly. | |
| It is telling people that without language skills this will be impossible. | |

# C

## Item 2

Alice is asking Thomas about his experiences when he spent some time travelling abroad with a friend after he had left school. (Society)

### Questions

MARKS

**a)** How long were they away for?

1

_____

**b)** Where exactly did they go?

2

_____

**c)** Alice asks Thomas about the qualities you should look for in a person you are going to travel with.

    **(i)** What does Thomas believe is the most important thing to allow two people to get on together?

1

    _____

    **(ii)** What would get in the way of people getting along?

1

    _____

**d)** Thomas talks about the issue of budgeting your money. Complete the sentence.

You have to fix ... and also have ...

2

_____

_____

**e)** Alice asks about travelling with a friend or family member.

    **(i)** Does Thomas think this is a good idea?

1

    _____

    **(ii)** What did he and Matthieu notice when they were away?

1

    _____

**f)** Why does Thomas think a group of two or three is best?

1

_____

**g)** Thomas discusses the advantages of travelling alone. State any **two** of them.

2

_____

_____

**(End of Listening paper)**

# Listening transcript

## Item 1

**(t)** **Item Number One**

You listen to this radio programme about going abroad for a holiday job.

**You now have one minute to study the questions for Item Number One.**

**(m)** Avant de chercher un job à l'étranger, il faut savoir un peu de la langue parlée dans le pays où vous voulez aller. Un boulot en contact avec le public (serveur, par exemple) nécessite un bon niveau de langue. Pour travailler en cuisine dans un restaurant, ou pour le ramassage de fruits et légumes, c'est moins important.

Travailler dans l'Union européenne est généralement moins compliqué. Pour un boulot de moins de trois mois, une carte d'identité ou un passeport suffisent. En dehors de l'Europe, vous devrez demander un visa de travail. Pour les jeunes qui rêvent de partir travailler au Canada, en Australie ou en Nouvelle-Zélande un visa gratuit est valable un an et permet de travailler (trois mois maximum pour le même employeur) tout en visitant le pays. Mais il faut posséder un billet d'avion retour et assez d'argent pour le début du séjour.

Pour plus de renseignements, allez faire des recherches dans un centre d'information jeunesse. Vous y trouverez les infos essentielles pour partir à l'étranger : des adresses utiles et des conseils pour rédiger votre CV.

*(2 minutes)*

# C

## Item 2

| | |
|---|---|
| **(t)** | **Item Number Two** |
| | Alice is asking Thomas about his experiences when he spent some time travelling abroad with a friend after he had left school. |
| | **You now have one minute to study the questions for Item Number Two.** |
| **(f)** | Salut Thomas : tu es de retour ! Comment s'est passé ton voyage avec Matthieu ? |
| **(m)** | Salut Alice ! C'était formidable ! Nous avons passé cinq mois ensemble, et nous nous sommes très bien entendus presque tout le temps. |
| **(f)** | Où étiez-vous ? |
| **(m)** | Nous avons passé quatre mois en Australie, où nous avons aussi travaillé, puis un mois au Japon pour faire du tourisme. |
| **(f)** | Tu as dit que tu t'es bien entendu avec Matthieu. Quelles qualités doit avoir la personne avec qui on décide de partir ? |
| **(m)** | La chose la plus importante, c'est la communication. La personne doit savoir dire ce qu'elle pense et ce qu'elle a envie de faire. Il faut se mettre d'accord sur ce que chacun veut faire avant de partir. Si l'un veut aller à la plage tout le temps et l'autre visiter les villes et les monuments, ça ne peut pas marcher. |
| **(f)** | Et l'argent, c'est important ? |
| **(m)** | Quand on part ensemble on doit avoir un budget assez similaire. Il est très important de connaître son budget à l'avance. Il faut se fixer une somme d'argent par jour et un budget pour les extras. |
| **(f)** | Est-ce que partir avec un ami ou un membre de sa famille, c'est plus simple ? |
| **(m)** | Non, pas forcément. C'est vrai que c'est plus simple de partir avec une personne qu'on connaît vraiment bien. Mais quand Matthieu et moi nous étions en voyage, nous avons souvent vu des groupes de copains se séparer. |
| **(f)** | Si on a peur de partir à deux, est-ce que partir à trois peut être une solution ? |
| **(m)** | Les groupes de deux ou trois personnes, pour moi, ça va. Cela reste une taille raisonnable. Plus le groupe est grand, plus les choses sont compliquées. |
| **(f)** | Et partir tout seul ? |
| **(m)** | Partir seul, c'est la liberté. Tu fais exactement ce que tu veux. Tu peux changer de programme sans problème. L'avantage d'être seul, c'est que quand on veut faire autre chose, on est complètement libre. |
| **(f)** | Merci. Maintenant, je veux organiser mon propre voyage ! |
| **(m)** | Bonne chance, Alice ! |
| | (*2 minutes*) |
| **(t)** | **End of test.** |
| | **Now look over your answers.** |

**(End of transcript)**

# National 5
# French

HODDER GIBSON
LEARN MORE

# Practice Paper A

## Reading

### Item 1

| Question | | Expected answer(s) | Mark | Hint | HTP |
|---|---|---|---|---|---|
| a) | (i) | The alarm from his pizzeria. | 1 | *Réveillé* means 'woken', so look after that for your answer. | Look at the advice on pages 22–8. |
| | (ii) | About 100 metres from the flat where he lived. | 1 | Give as much information as you can. | |
| b) | | Put on a T-shirt, trousers and shoes / ran there (to the pizzeria). | 2 | Give as many details as you can; there are 2 marks for this. | |
| c) | | There were four people / they were stealing (taking) money and equipment. | 2 | Give as many details as you can; there are 2 marks for this. | |
| d) | (i) | Hid in the toilets / called the police. | 2 | Give as many details as you can; there are 2 marks for this. | |
| | (ii) | He felt threatened by the owner. | 1 | You could look up 'threaten' in the English side of the dictionary: this will give you *menacer*. | |
| e) | | They fled and have not been identified.<br>First box ticked. | 1 | The equivalent of 'two others' (*deux autres*) shows you where to find the answer; avoid jumping to conclusions based on one word such as *fureur*. | |

### Item 2

| Question | | Expected answer(s) | Mark | Hint | HTP |
|---|---|---|---|---|---|
| a) | | He had fallen ill / he had a heart attack. | 1 | Read all the questions first, then look through the whole text before you start to answer this; it should then be clear which is the correct answer. Look for *père* at the start, and use your dictionary if you need to afterwards. | Look at the advice on pages 22–8. |
| b) | | The young boy set off to warn his mother.<br>Third box ticked. | 1 | Again, if you have read all the questions first, then looked through the whole text, it should be clear which is the correct answer. | |
| c) | (i) | On Wednesday evening / at (about) 22.30 (10.30 at night). | 2 | Give the details as carefully as you can, and watch those clock times! | Look at the vocabulary on pages 73–5. |

| Question | | Expected answer(s) | Mark | Hint | HTP |
|---|---|---|---|---|---|
| | (ii) | He was wearing pyjamas / he was very cold. (any one) | 1 | 'Any one' means there are more than one: choose the answer you are most sure of. | Look at the advice on pages 22–8. |
| d) | | He had left home to find *his mother* who was *at work (in a factory)*. | 2 | Make sure you get the correct place, then be careful to get the correct words, especially *sa* (his), and *usine* (factory) (find it in the dictionary!). | |
| e) | | Less than / under half an hour. | 1 | Watch out for *moins de* (less than). The details are important. | |
| f) | | To thank him / to tell him her husband was out of hospital. | 2 | Give as many details as you can; there are 2 marks for this. | |

# Item 3

| Question | | Expected answer(s) | Mark | Hint | HTP |
|---|---|---|---|---|---|
| a) | | To be enthusiastic. | 1 | Look for words describing feelings or emotions at the start, as this is the first question! | Look at the vocabulary on pages 73–5. |
| b) | | It should be a regular activity / better ten minutes every day / than an intensive week, then nothing. (any two) | 2 | Give as many details as you can; there are two marks for this. 'Any two' means there are more than two, but play safe if you are not sure what the answer might be! | |
| c) | (i) | Learning off by heart. | 1 | *Beaucoup pensent* (many think) should show you where to look. The words *par cœur* should be in the dictionary, under *cœur*. | |
| | (ii) | It is no use if you have a new conversation topic. | 1 | The word *mais* (but) is a clue as to where to find the answer. | |
| d) | (i) | Wishing to have / perfect pronunciation and grammar. | 2 | The word *absurde* is a clue as to where to look; there are 2 marks, so give details. | |
| | (ii) | Don't make that your priority / be brave (courageous) / don't be afraid of making mistakes. (any two) | 2 | Again, look at the word *mais* (but) and look for your answer after that, making sure to give as many details as you can. | Look at the advice on pages 22–8. |
| e) | | It is trying to get people to be realistic about language learning. Second box ticked. | 1 | The text should have shown you that the first statement is not correct, as mention is made of problems when learning, and there is no mention of a company name, so you should ignore the third statement. | |

# Writing

The assessment criteria for writing are shown below, but you may have to take your writing to your teacher to get an idea of what mark it would get. However, you should bear the following points in mind.

- You will always have to write an email, so there is no need to learn formal starts and ends to letters.
- There are six bullet points to answer; the first four are predictable, the last two vary from year to year.
- Each bullet point should have between 15 and 30 words to address it properly.
- For the first four bullet points, you can have answers more or less prepared; however, you have to look carefully at the details of the job/work experience being offered, and slightly change your prepared material for bullet points three and four to fit.
- To get a mark of 'good' or 'very good', you must address the last two bullet points properly; that means making sure you look at the job being offered, and also making sure you answer the points raised in the two bullet points.
- It is very likely that one of the two bullet points will require you to ask questions, so make sure you can do this properly; practise writing questions on a number of areas.
- You should aim to have at least 15 words for each of these last two points.
- You will be assessed on how well you have answered the points, and on the accuracy of your language, so leave some time to go over your answers and check the spelling, accents and verb endings in particular.
- For a mark of 'good' or 'very good', you should have some complex language, for example, longer, varied sentences that include conjunctions such as *parce que* with sub-clauses, and adjectives attached to nouns, if you can.

| Assessment criteria for writing | | | | |
|---|---|---|---|---|
| Category | Mark | Content | Accuracy | Language resource – variety, range, structures |
| Very good | 20 | The job advert has been addressed in a full and balanced way. The candidate uses detailed language.<br><br>The candidate addresses the advert completely and competently, including **information in response to both unpredictable bullet points**.<br><br>A range of verbs/verb forms, tenses and constructions is used.<br><br>Overall this comes over as a competent, well thought-out and serious application for the job. | The candidate handles all aspects of grammar and spelling accurately, although the language may contain one or two minor errors.<br><br>Where the candidate attempts to use language more appropriate to Higher, a slightly higher number of inaccuracies need not detract from the overall very good impression. | The candidate is comfortable with the first person of the verb and generally uses a different verb in each sentence.<br><br>Some modal verbs and infinitives may be used.<br><br>There is good use of adjectives, adverbs and prepositional phrases and, where appropriate, word order. There may be a range of tenses.<br><br>The candidate uses co-ordinating conjunctions and/or subordinate clauses where appropriate.<br><br>The language of the email flows well. |

**A**

| Assessment criteria for writing | | | | |
|---|---|---|---|---|
| Category | Mark | Content | Accuracy | Language resource – variety, range, structures |
| Good | 16 | The job advert has been addressed competently.<br><br>There is less evidence of detailed language.<br><br>The candidate uses a reasonable range of verbs/verb forms.<br><br>Overall, the candidate has produced a genuine, reasonably accurate attempt at applying for the specific job, **even though he/she may not address one of the unpredictable bullet points**. | The candidate handles a range of verbs fairly accurately.<br><br>There are some errors in spelling, adjective endings and, where relevant, case endings. Use of accents is less secure, where appropriate.<br><br>Where the candidate is attempting to use more complex vocabulary and structures, these may be less successful, although basic structures are used accurately.<br><br>There may be one or two examples of inaccurate dictionary use, especially in the unpredictable bullet points. | There may be repetition of verbs.<br><br>There may be examples of listing, in particular when referring to school/college experience, without further amplification.<br><br>There may be one or two examples of a co-ordinating conjunction, but most sentences are simple sentences.<br><br>The candidate keeps to more basic vocabulary, particularly in response to either or both unpredictable bullet points. |
| Satisfactory | 12 | The job advert has been addressed fairly competently.<br><br>The candidate makes limited use of detailed language.<br><br>The language is fairly repetitive and uses a limited range of verbs and fixed phrases, e.g. 'I like', 'I go', 'I play'.<br><br>The candidate copes fairly well with areas of personal details, education, skills, interests and work experience but does not deal fully with the two unpredictable bullet points **and indeed may not address either or both of the unpredictable bullet points**.<br><br>On balance, however, the candidate has produced a satisfactory job application in the specific language. | The verbs are generally correct, but may be repetitive.<br><br>There are quite a few errors in other parts of speech – gender of nouns, cases, singular/plural confusion, for instance.<br><br>Prepositions may be missing, e.g. 'I go the town.'<br><br>Overall, there is more correct than incorrect. | The candidate copes with the first and third person of a few verbs, where appropriate.<br><br>A limited range of verbs is used.<br><br>Sentences are basic and mainly brief.<br><br>There is minimal use of adjectives, probably mainly after 'is', e.g. 'Chemistry is interesting.'<br><br>The candidate has a weak knowledge of plurals.<br><br>There may be several spelling errors, e.g. reversal of vowel combinations. |

| Assessment criteria for writing | | | | |
|---|---|---|---|---|
| Category | Mark | Content | Accuracy | Language resource – variety, range, structures |
| Unsatisfactory | 8 | The job advert has been addressed in an uneven manner and/or with insufficient use of detailed language.<br><br>The language is repetitive, e.g. 'I like', 'I go', 'I play' may feature several times.<br><br>There may be little difference between Satisfactory and Unsatisfactory.<br><br>**Either or both of the unpredictable bullet points may not have been addressed**.<br><br>There may be one sentence which is not intelligible to a sympathetic native speaker. | Ability to form tenses is inconsistent.<br><br>There are errors in many other parts of speech – gender of nouns, cases, singular/plural confusion, for instance.<br><br>Several errors are serious, perhaps showing mother tongue interference.<br><br>The detail in the unpredictable bullet points may be very weak.<br><br>Overall, there is more incorrect than correct. | The candidate mainly copes only with the personal language required in bullet points 1 and 2.<br><br>The verbs 'is' and 'study' may also be used correctly.<br><br>Sentences are basic.<br><br>An English word may appear in the writing.<br><br>There may be an example of serious dictionary misuse. |
| Poor | 4 | The candidate has had considerable difficulty in addressing the job advert. There is little evidence of the use of detailed language.<br><br>Three or four sentences may not be understood by a sympathetic native speaker.<br><br>**Either or both of the unpredictable bullet points may not have been addressed**. | Many of the verbs are incorrect.<br><br>There are many errors in other parts of speech – personal pronouns, gender of nouns, cases, singular/plural confusion, prepositions, for instance.<br><br>The language is probably inaccurate throughout the writing. | The candidate cannot cope with more than one or two basic verbs.<br><br>The candidate displays almost no knowledge of the present tense of verbs.<br><br>Verbs used more than once may be written differently on each occasion.<br><br>Sentences are very short.<br><br>The candidate has a very limited vocabulary.<br><br>Several English words may appear in the writing.<br><br>There are examples of serious dictionary misuse. |

| | Assessment criteria for writing | | | |
|---|---|---|---|---|
| Category | Mark | Content | Accuracy | Language resource – variety, range, structures |
| Very poor | 0 | The candidate is unable to address the job advert. **The two unpredictable bullet points may not have been addressed**. Very little is intelligible to a sympathetic native speaker. | Virtually nothing is correct. | The candidate may only cope with the verbs 'to have' and 'to be'. Very few words are written correctly in the modern language. English words are used. There may be several examples of mother tongue interference. There may be several examples of serious dictionary misuse. |

# Listening

## Item 1

| Question | | Expected answer(s) | Mark | Hint | HTP |
|---|---|---|---|---|---|
| a) | | Shops to open on Sundays. | 1 | Make sure you know the days of the week! | |
| b) | (i) | (They will receive) an additional 110% of their salary on Sundays or double the salary for evenings. | 1 | Read the question to give an idea of the meaning of the text! Work at your numbers; there are always some in listenings. Times of day are important too! Get them right. | Look at the vocabulary on pages 73–5. |
| | (ii) | Zara will pay for the childcare of / employees who have children. OR They will pay for a taxi home / for people who cannot use public transport. | 2 | Choose the answer you are more sure of, but give as many details as you can. | Look at the advice on page 40. |
| c) | | By 10 p.m. / 22.00. | 1 | Remember to work at your times and numbers; there are always some in listenings. | Look at the vocabulary on pages 73–5. |
| d) | | About 30. | 1 | Recognise the ending -aine on a number; it means 'about'. | |

| Question | | Expected answer(s) | Mark | Hint | HTP |
|---|---|---|---|---|---|
| e) | | They can choose not to open. OR They can call on employees from another store in the same area. | 1 | Choose the answer you are more sure of, but give as many details as you can. | Look at the advice on page 40. |
| f) | | The reporter is giving a neutral report of what has been agreed. Third box ticked. | 1 | Look at your previous answers to give you an idea of what is the best overall answer. | |

# Item 2

| Question | | Expected answer(s) | Mark | Hint | HTP |
|---|---|---|---|---|---|
| a) | (i) | She is not tired. | 1 | Read the question to give you an idea of what the passage is about before you listen! | Look at the advice on page 40. |
| | (ii) | It was a chance to earn more / she earned 300 € extra / for working four evenings. (any two) | 2 | Choose the answer you are more sure of, but give as many details as you can and get the numbers right! Write them down in your notes. | Look at the vocabulary on pages 73–5. |
| b) | | Working conditions are better on Sundays / people are much more relaxed / people are happy to stroll around (chat to them). (any two) | 2 | Choose the answer you are more sure of, but give as many details as you can. Again, if you have read the questions, it will be easier to identify the answers. | |
| c) | | There are good financial reasons / it offers employment / things (habits) have changed / the traditional Sunday family meal does not always happen. (any two) | 2 | Choose the answer you are more sure of, but give as many details as you can. Again, if you have read the questions, it will be easier to identify the answers. | |
| d) | (i) | People should be allowed to work if they want to. | 1 | If you have read the questions, it will be easier to identify the answers. Make sure you give as many details as you can! | |
| | (ii) | She was happy to work on a Sunday as she got triple pay. | 1 | If you have read the questions, it will be easier to identify the answers. Make sure you give as many details as you can! | Look at the advice on page 40. |
| e) | | She wants to be with her family / she has three young children / there are already lots of shops open on Sundays / we should preserve family life. (any one) | 1 | Choose the answer you are more sure of, but give as many details as you can. Again, if you have read the questions, it will be easier to identify the answers. | |
| f) | | Pressure might be put on people who refuse to work on Sundays. | 1 | Make the link between *pression* and pressure and it works! | |
| g) | | In a city like Paris, shops should be open every day. Second box ticked. | 1 | If you have read the questions, you will be listening out for *japonaise* to identify the answer. | |

# Practice Paper B

## Reading

### Item 1

| Question | | Expected answer(s) | Mark | Hint | HTP |
|---|---|---|---|---|---|
| a) | (i) | If you practise a sport. | 1 | *Besoin* means need: look after that for your answer. Always use the words in the question to help you. | Look at the vocabulary on pages 77–8 for 'Lifestyles'. |
| | (ii) | It is necessary for the proper functioning of the body (brain). | 1 | Look out for the equivalent of 'three or four meals', and your answer should be just after that. | |
| b) | | Lunch and dinner should contain a *source of / some protein*, some *vegetables*, a dairy product and a piece of fruit. | 2 | You have some flexibility in the correct answer. | |
| c) | (i) | Cheaply / for a modest price / you can get a balanced meal. | 2 | The question is a good guide as to where to look. There are 2 marks for this, so give as many details as you can. | |
| | (ii) | They provide vitamins and fibre. | 1 | Although this question is worth only 1 mark, both details are necessary; the question did not say 'any **one** thing'. | |
| d) | (i) | The food is fatty / it is not very nutritional. | 1 | Choose the answer you are more sure of. | |
| | (ii) | You can / should use them once a week (at most). | 1 | Again, you have some flexibility. | |
| e) | | To encourage students to eat healthily. Third box ticked. | 1 | While all three things are correct, only the third one covers the whole article. | |

### Item 2

| Question | Expected answer(s) | Mark | Hint | HTP |
|---|---|---|---|---|
| a) | A list of the areas or topics to revise for each subject / your strengths and weaknesses / questions for your teacher. (any two) | 2 | Choose the answers you are most sure of. | Look at the advice on pages 22–8. |
| b) | Don't take on too much, you might be discouraged. If you have an auditory memory, taking part in lessons is a great help. First and fourth boxes ticked. | 2 | The word *différent* is not anywhere in the passage. *Ne sont pas le seul moyen* means 'are not the only way' rather than 'not the best way'. | |

| Question | | Expected answer(s) | Mark | Hint | HTP |
|---|---|---|---|---|---|
| c) | | Use sketches (mindmaps) / use colours to mark up your revision notes / add your own comments to your notes. (any two) | 2 | Remember to use the glossary words! | Look at the advice on pages 22–8. |
| d) | (i) | Get enough sleep / go to bed at regular times. | 1 | Either answer will do. | |
| | (ii) | Don't miss out meals / eat a balanced diet / do sport. (any one) | 1 | Choose the answer you are most sure of. | |
| e) | (i) | Mobile / computer / TV. (any one) | 1 | Remember, one is enough, but you can put down two if you want to be sure. | |
| | (ii) | Music in the background. | 1 | When you look up *fond* in the dictionary, skim down the entry and you will come across *fond musical*: 'background music'. | |

# Item 3

| Question | | Expected answer(s) | Mark | Hint | HTP |
|---|---|---|---|---|---|
| a) | | Seventeen (years old). | 1 | Make sure you get the numbers right. | Look at the vocabulary on pages 73–5. |
| b) | | To practise his English. | 1 | 'Why' means you are looking for a reason, so words like *parce que* or *pour* are what to look for. | Look at the advice on pages 22–8. |
| c) | (i) | He was very young to travel abroad alone. OR He didn't have much money. OR The organisation covered all his costs. | 1 | Choose an answer that makes sense, and then give as many details as you can. | |
| | (ii) | Four weeks. | 1 | Make sure you get the numbers right. | Look at the vocabulary on pages 73–5. |
| | (iii) | Different countries in Europe and from all over the USA. | 2 | Here, the little details are important, so make sure you include them. | |
| d) | | They looked after a park and built a hut. The four weeks really improved his English. First and fourth boxes ticked. | 2 | Watch out for the tricks: just because 'afternoons' is in the passage, it does not mean that is the answer. | Look at the advice on pages 22–8. |
| e) | (i) | Very average. | 1 | Make sure you get the correct meaning of *moyen* in the dictionary. | |
| | (ii) | Keeping up his friendships. OR Keeping his English at a good level. | 1 | Choose the answer you are more sure of. | |

# Writing

Please see the answer section for Writing in Paper A on pages 49–52.

# Listening

## Item 1

| Question | | Expected answer(s) | Mark | Hint | HTP |
|---|---|---|---|---|---|
| a) | | Your teacher(s).<br>OR<br>Careers (guidance) staff. | 1 | One mark, so one person / set of people is enough. | Look at the vocabulary on pages 81–5. |
| b) | (i) | Go to open days.<br>OR<br>Look at the information colleges publish. | 1 | Choose the answer you are more sure of. | Look at the advice on page 40. |
| | (ii) | Apply for a place. | 1 | It makes sense, so think about how things work in real life! | |
| c) | (i) | Send you an offer (by post or email). | 1 | It makes sense, so think about how things work in real life! | |
| | (ii) | Your CV.<br>OR<br>Your school report (exam results). | 1 | Choose the answer you are more sure of, and remember it should make sense! | |
| | (iii) | 2nd April. | 1 | Get dates and numbers right; write them down as notes, so you can check in the third listening. | Look at the vocabulary on pages 73–5. |
| d) | | There is an extra process starting in June / the unfilled places are offered in June. | 1 | There is more then one potential answer, so choose one you are happy with. | Look at the advice on page 40. |
| e) | | It is explaining the steps a young person in the last year of school should take.<br>Second box ticked. | 1 | Look at your answers to the previous questions to help you decide which is correct. | |

# Item 2

| Question | | Expected answer(s) | Mark | Hint | HTP |
|---|---|---|---|---|---|
| **a)** | **(i)** | Agriculture. | **1** | It sounds very similar. | |
| | **(ii)** | She wasn't earning enough (to live on). | **1** | You need to know *gagner* is 'to earn'. | Look at the vocabulary on pages 84–5. |
| **b)** | **(i)** | The electricity was not working in her bathroom.<br>OR<br>She needed something done and thought, 'I could do that.' | **1** | Knowing basic vocabulary like the rooms of a house is a help. | Look at the advice on page 40. |
| | **(ii)** | Four years ago. | **1** | Numbers, times and dates are often very important, but easy to get wrong! Write them in your notes and check on the third listening. | Look at the vocabulary on pages 73–5. |
| **c)** | | She was the only female on the course.<br>OR<br>Some of the others thought she should not be there. | **1** | Choose the answer you are more sure of. | Look at the advice on page 40. |
| **d)** | | The training lasted for *three years*, then I spent a year working for Jean-Claude, before *starting to work for myself*. | **2** | Numbers again! | Look at the vocabulary on pages 73–5. |
| **e)** | | She looks after her animals until 12, then works as an electrician for a few hours in the afternoon. | **2** | Watch those times and times of day! | |
| **f)** | | Plumber<br>Joiner<br>First and fourth boxes ticked. | **2** | If you don't know these trades, it is worth learning some, as it is part of 'employability'. | Look at the vocabulary on pages 83–4. |
| **g)** | | By word of mouth.<br>OR<br>Customers recommend her.<br>OR<br>Through friends of friends. | **1** | 1 mark, so one answer is enough! | Look at the advice on page 40. |

# Practice Paper C

## Reading

### Item 1

| Question | | Expected answer(s) | Mark | Hint | HTP |
|---|---|---|---|---|---|
| a) | (i) | To be more active. | 1 | Use the question to see where to look. | Look at the vocabulary on pages 77–8. |
| | (ii) | Those who are overweight / obese. | 1 | Note how close *obésité* is to English. | |
| | (iii) | It encourages people to be more (physically) active. OR It helps against the tendency to sit still. | 1 | Choose the answer you are more sure of, but do give details. Note that the three questions are all sub-parts of the overall question, so all the answers should be in one paragraph. | |
| b) | | A hot or cold drink A yoghurt First and third boxes ticked. | 2 | Look carefully at the details. Make sure you only tick two boxes! | Look at the advice on pages 22–8. |
| c) | (i) | Get them better marks at school. | 1 | Look for *enfants* to find the answer. | |
| | (ii) | A link has been established between having breakfast and results in school / pupils who have a healthy breakfast / are twice as likely to be above average in marks (as those who do not have a healthy breakfast). (any two) | 2 | For this answer, the details are important. When you are told 'give details', write a longer answer. | Look at the vocabulary on pages 77–8. |
| d) | | Sweets / crisps / fizzy drinks / other less healthy food. (any two) | 2 | Choose the answers you are sure of, but do give details where you need to. | Look at the advice on pages 22–8. |

### Item 2

| Question | | Expected answer(s) | Mark | Hint | HTP |
|---|---|---|---|---|---|
| a) | | They want to avoid their pupils going outside the buildings / at a time of terrorist risks / schools are under a state of emergency / the government has declared a state of emergency. | 2 | You have quite a lot of leeway here, as long as you understand the basic situation; just give as many details as you can to make sure you get the two marks. | Look at the advice on pages 22–8. |
| b) | | They have received threats. | 1 | *Certains* means 'some', so that is where you can find the answer. Be careful with *menaces* – use your dictionary. | |

| Question | | Expected answer(s) | Mark | Hint | HTP |
|---|---|---|---|---|---|
| c) | | They want their pupils to be able to *smoke in the playground* and not in the street at *break time (during intervals)*. | 2 | Knowing basic school vocabulary helps a lot in Learning topics. | Look at the vocabulary on pages 81–3. |
| d) | | The rules do not allow it / smoking (on school grounds) is forbidden / it is against Education Ministry rules. | 1 | Again, you have quite a lot of leeway here, as long as you understand the basic situation; just give as many details as you can to make sure you get the mark. | Look at the vocabulary on pages 81–3. |
| e) | (i) | Proposed smoking zones in school during break times | 1 | Look after *organisée* for your answer. | |
| | (ii) | They have refused to allow it. | 1 | *Santé* is 'health': that is where to find the answer. | |
| f) | (i) | They think pupil safety is more important than rules. | 1 | Look for 'head teachers' in French to see where the answer is. | |
| | (ii) | They have gone ahead and organised smoking zones during break times. | 1 | Give as many details as you can. | |

# Item 3

| Question | | Expected answer(s) | Mark | Hint | HTP |
|---|---|---|---|---|---|
| a) | | Ten months. | 1 | Make sure you get numbers, times, etc. right! | Look at the vocabulary on pages 73–5. |
| b) | | She was looking after / about a hundred children in difficulties / aged from six to sixteen / in a social centre in the capital. | 2 | There are lots of possibilities – just go for as many details as you can work out. | |
| c) | (i) | The language. | 1 | *Langue* is an important word to know. | |
| | (ii) | She learned the language, bit by bit / she became integrated / she fitted in quickly / she made friends. | 1 | There is a bit of flexibility here, so just concentrate on giving the details you can easily find. | |
| d) | | Armenia has economic and political problems / young people, though, want to succeed / it is mountainous and very beautiful / it changes every season / it is very peaceful so she could hitch-hike easily. | 2 | Lots of possible answers, but don't try to give them all. Choose two or three where you are confident of all the details. | Look at the advice on pages 22–8. |
| e) | | She learned a lot / she has managed to get an administrative job / she is starting her new post in a fortnight. | 2 | Again, several answers are possible, but choose the two where you are more sure of the details. | |
| f) | | She enjoyed her experience and learned a lot from it. Third box ticked. | 1 | Your overall answers should help you with your choice. | |

# Writing

Please see the answer section for Writing in Paper A on pages 49–52.

# Listening

## Item 1

| Question | | Expected answer(s) | Mark | Hint | HTP |
|---|---|---|---|---|---|
| a) | (i) | A bit of the language of the country you are going to. | 1 | *Savoir* is 'to know': listen carefully after you hear that word. | Look at the vocabulary on pages 84–6. |
| | (ii) | The kitchen of a restaurant / picking fruit (or vegetables). (either one) | 1 | Choose the one you are more sure of, but give details. | Look at the advice on page 40. |
| b) | | An ID card.<br>OR<br>A passport. | 1 | Choose the one you are more sure of. | |
| c) | (i) | One year. | 1 | Listen carefully to the numbers and write the answer down as a note. Make sure you know the words for 'day', 'month', 'year', etc. | Look at the vocabulary on pages 73–5. |
| | (ii) | Work while visiting the country. | 1 | Watch out for that 'false friend', *travailler*: it means 'work', not 'travel'. | |
| | (iii) | A return air ticket / enough money for the beginning of the trip. (either one) | 1 | Choose the one you are more sure of. | Look at the advice on page 40. |
| d) | | Essential informational / useful addresses / advice on writing a CV. (any one) | 1 | Choose the one you are more sure of, but give details. | |
| e) | | It is giving clear advice to help young people find work abroad.<br>First box ticked. | 1 | Although all three answers could be right, only the first one reflects the overall purpose. | |

# Item 2

| Question | | Expected answer(s) | Mark | Hint | HTP |
|---|---|---|---|---|---|
| a) | | Five months. | 1 | Watch out for those numbers and time words! | Look at the vocabulary on pages 73–5. |
| b) | | Australia, then Japan. | 2 | Even if you are not sure, you can guess from the French. | |
| c) | (i) | (Good) communication. | 1 | Listen carefully after the word for 'important'. | Look at the advice on page 40. |
| | (ii) | Not agreeing on what to do / if one always wants to go to the beach and the other wants to visit sights and towns. (either answer) | 1 | Sometimes you have to give details to get the mark – there are no half-marks! | |
| d) | | You have to fix *a sum to spend every day* and also have *a budget for extra things*. | 2 | Look at the question as you are listening, and pick up on the key words for 'fix' and 'budget', remembering they will be pronounced in French! | |
| e) | (i) | Not necessarily / it is easier to travel with someone you know. (either one) | 1 | Two different answers, but both are correct! | Look at the vocabulary on pages 85–6. |
| | (ii) | Groups of friends split up. | 1 | Make sure you give the details. | |
| f) | | Bigger groups make things more complicated. | 1 | Follow Alice's questions, and pick up the answer after each one. | |
| g) | | You can do exactly what you want / you can change your plans easily / if you want to do something, you are free to do so / it gives you freedom. (any two) | 2 | Choose the two you are most sure of, but give details; if you are not sure, give as much information as you can. | |